THE STORY
OF OUR
FAMILY
IN THE
TWENTIETH
CENTURY

FOUR SEASONS
PUBLISHING

$\mathcal{C}$ONTENTS

Using this Book 3

People to Contact 5

The 1900s: The Nation in the 1900s 6

             The Family in the 1900s 8

The 1910s: The Nation in the 1910s 10

             The Family in the 1910s 12

The 1920s: The Nation in the 1920s 14

             The Family in the 1920s 16

The 1930s: The Nation in the 1930s 18

             The Family in the 1930s 20

The 1940s: The Nation in the 1940s 22

             The Family in the 1940s 24

The 1950s: The Nation in the 1950s 26

             The Family in the 1950s 28

The 1960s: The Nation in the 1960s 30

             The Family in the 1960s 32

The 1970s: The Nation in the 1970s 34

             The Family in the 1970s 36

The 1980s: The Nation in the 1980s 38

             The Family in the 1980s 40

The 1990s: The Nation in the 1990s 42

             The Family in the 1990s 44

2000 and beyond 46

Family Tree 48

Other Relations 52

Special Friends 53

Additional Photographs 54

USING THIS BOOK

Every family has a unique story to tell and every family's story is worth telling.

This book makes it easy for you to compile the story of your own family during the twentieth century, a century of extraordinary changes. It provides you with two large pages for each of the ten decades, with spaces for mementoes, cuttings and photographs, as well as questions to encourage your own writing.

Because *every* family is always part of the nation, its personal story takes place within the context of national events, values and fashions. So, in the book, pages portraying the nation's story during this remarkable century interleave the story of your own family. These pages show dozens of real objects which were current and popular at the time or relate to significant events. They also show the dates on which important or amusing incidents occurred, details of what typical items cost and how things gradually changed as the decades rolled by.

Towards the end of the book are four pages you can use to make a simple Family Tree. If there are other relatives you want to mention, or friends who are not relations but who have played an important part in the life of the family, there are pages for them too.

You may also like to consider who would enjoy contributing to the writing of the family's story or who can help you fill in any gaps in your knowledge. Many people will be delighted to share their memories with you. Page 5 gives you space to list them.

Whatever you write and however you set about it, you can be entirely confident that you will earn the gratitude of both present and future generations in recording for them an aspect of their heritage which they will find increasingly difficult to compile for themselves. You can also enjoy the pleasure of knowing that you are creating something entirely unique.

Acknowledgements

The great majority of the illustrations and items reproduced in this book are from the Robert Opie Collection in Gloucester Docks, Gloucestershire. Mr Opie has given considerable help in the compilation and preparation of this book and we are most grateful to him.

Other Sources of Help

If you want to delve more deeply into your family's history but are not sure how to set about it, you may wish to consult some of the books and magazines designed to help. Those listed below are just a small selection of the many easily obtainable.

"The Family Historian's Enquire Within" by Pauline Saul. The Federation of Family History Societies 1995. ISBN 187 209 483X.

"The Family Tree Detective" by Colin D. Rogers. Manchester University Press 1986. ISBN 0 7190 1846 3.

"The Oxford Guide to Family History" by David Hay. Oxford University Press 1993. ISBN 0 1986 91777.

Family History Monthly. Diamond Publishing Group Ltd., 45 St Mary's Road, London W5 5RQ.

Family Tree Magazine. J.M. and M. Armstrong & Partners, 6 Great Whyte Ramsey, Huntingdon, Cambridgeshire, PE17 1HL.

PEOPLE TO CONTACT

You may wish to get in touch with close acquaintances and relatives to ask them about their memories and impressions of different periods. You could make a list below of all the people you would like to contact.

NAME	ADDRESS AND TELEPHONE NUMBER	✓

The Nation in the 1900s

In the 1900s

- The population in 1901 was 36,999,946.
- In 1904 there were 8465 private cars on the road.
- In 1906 a train driver typically earned £2 5s.9d. a week and a coal miner about £1 11s.5d.
- Prices: in 1903, a pint of beer cost 2d., 1lb of tea 1s.6d., 'The Times' 3d. and postage for an inland letter 1d.
- Rudyard Kipling's *Just So Stories* and Beatrix Potter's *Peter Rabbit* were immediate successes when they were published in 1902.
- J. M. Barrie's *Peter Pan* was among the most successful new plays of the decade.
- Popular songs included *Shine on Harvest Moon*, *Sweet Adeline* and *Give my Regards to Broadway*.

1900	Coca Cola first sold in the UK
1900	'Daily Express' first published
1900	British Labour Party founded
1900	Siege of Mafeking relieved by British forces under Baden-Powell
1901	Commonwealth of Australia formed
1901	King Camp Gillette patents safety razor
1901	Queen Victoria dies, aged 81
1901	The London United Tramways launch first electric trams
1901	Brownie camera No. 2 goes on sale
1902	Underground Electric Railway Company formed
1902	Empire Day first celebrated
1902	Boer War ends in British victory
1902	Coronation of King Edward VII
1902	First conviction made in Britain on evidence of fingerprints
1903	First radio message transmitted from England to USA
1903	'Daily Mirror' first published
1903	First motor taxis appear in London
1904	Electric mainline train service opens
1904	Registration plates first used on motor cars
1904	Books of postage stamps issued
1905	Automobile Association formed
1905	Footballers' maximum wage set at £4 per week
1905	Sinn Fein founded by Arthur Griffith
1906	Trade Disputes Act legalises peaceful picketing
1907	Brooklands motor racing track opens
1907	Boy-Scout movement founded by Baden-Powell
1908	England win first-ever international football match, against Austria
1908	Old-age pension of 5s.0d. a week granted to single people over 70
1908	Olympic Games held in London
1909	Victoria and Albert Museum opens in Kensington, London
1909	Louis Bleriot flies his monoplane across English Channel
1909	First Woolworth's store opens, in Liverpool

The Family
in the 1900s

Did any of your relations serve in the Boer War? **O**r overseas in the Empire?

....

....

....

....

....

....

....

....

....

....

❧ Important Family Events ❧

NAME	DATE	EVENT

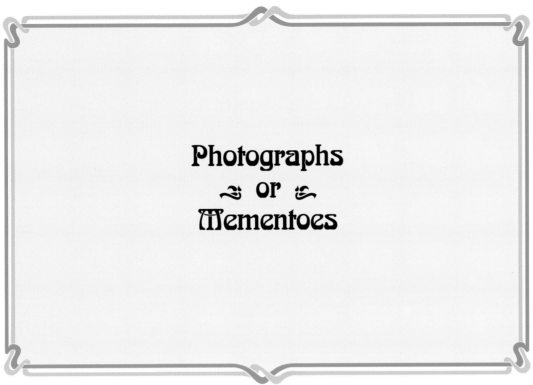

Photographs or Mementoes

Did any of them speak about the death of Queen Victoria or the coronation of King Edward VII?

Did any of them tell you of the first time they saw an aeroplane or a motor car? **D**o you have any mementoes from that time?

The Nation in the 1910s

~~~ In the 1910s ~~~

- The 1911 census showed a population of 40,831,396.
- In 1914 there were 132,015 private cars.
- In 1913 the monthly salary for a teacher was about £15 0s.0d. and the weekly wage for a train driver was £2 0s.6d.
- Prices: by 1915, the price of a pint of beer had risen to 3d., 1lb of tea to 2s.0d. 'The Times' was still 3d. and inland letter postage 1d.
- The *Birth of a Nation* was the biggest-earning film and Bernard Shaw's new play *Pygmalion* was a West End success.
- *Alexander's Ragtime Band* and *Chinatown, My Chinatown* were two of the most popular songs.

1910 King Edward VII dies

1910 Dr Crippen hanged in London for poisoning his wife

1910 First Labour Exchanges open

1911 First trolley-buses appear

1911 MP's annual salary fixed at £400

1911 Coronation of King George V

1911 Suffragettes riot in Whitehall

1911 First National Health Bill introduced

1912 Captain Scott dies on way back from South Pole

1912 'Titanic' sinks after hitting an iceberg, with loss of 1513 lives

1912 National Insurance introduced

1913 Sickness, unemployment and maternity benefits introduced

1913 Charlie Chaplin makes his first film

1914 Britain declares war on Germany

1914 Panama Canal opens

1914 Builders', miners' and railway workers' strike

1914 Single bomb dropped on Dover – Britain's first air-raid

1915 Photos first required in British passports

1915 Germany uses poison gas for first time, at Ypres

1915 Passenger liner 'Lusitania' torpedoed by Germans, with loss of 1198 lives

1915 First air-raid on London

1915 The Women's Institute founded

1915 Edith Cavell shot by German firing squad

1916 Military conscription begins

1916 Easter rebellion in Dublin against British rule

1916 Military tanks first used in the British army

1916 First Battle of the Somme results in 420,000 casualties

1917 United States declares war on Germany

1918 Women first permitted to vote in Britain

1918 Royal Air Force formed

1918 First World War ends

1919 First British airline opens with two-seater single-engine biplane

1919 First meeting of League of Nations in Paris

The Family
in the 1910s

Which members of the family served in the First World War? **W**hat descriptions did they give of life during those years?

....

....

....

....

....

....

....

....

....

....

....

....

~~~ Photographs ~~~

∿ Important Family Events ∿

NAME	DATE	EVENT

At home, in what way did life change because of the war? And what was it like immediately after the war ended?

Can any of your relations remember hearing about the sinking of the 'Titanic', or the coronation of King George V?

Did any of them join the newly-formed Women's Institute?

THE NATION IN THE 1920s

I'M LITTLE MISS NOBODY AT WORK—

Doing the FOX TROT.

The SCHNEIDER TROPHY CONTEST 1929
Sept. 6th & 7th

BANK HOLIDAY WHERE TO GO

BY TRAIN, TRAM AND MOTOR BUS
AUGUST 1926

You have to wash your Neck when you've got your hair Bobbed.

ROYAL AERO CLUB

Miss 1927

R 100

TRAFFIC ON
BRITISH MANUFACTURE

Meltis LITTLE PRINCESS
Assorted Chocolates
Meltis LTD.
BEDFORD & LONDON, ENGLAND.
HALF POUND (INCLUDING FOILS)
PHOTO BY MARCUS ADAMS

Royal Enfield
MADE LIKE A GUN

THE FAMOUS 6 H.P. ROYAL ENFIELD

"FELIX KEPT UNK"

1928-9 HORNBY BOOK OF TRAINS

6100

PRICE THREEPENCE

⬟ IN THE 1920s ⬟

• In 1921 the population of Great Britain was 42,769,196.
• By 1924 the number of private cars had increased to 482,356.
• In 1920, a GP earned on average £756 a year and a farm worker £1 17s.10d. a week.
• In 1923 you would have paid 10d. for 8 Players No.3 cigarettes and £175 for a 2-seater Morris Cowley. In 1927 a radio licence cost 10s.0d.
• The most popular names for babies born in 1925 were Joan and John.
• 1920s hits included: the play *The Ghost Train*; the film *The Jazz Singer* (the first full-length talkie); the song *Avalon*; the fox-trot and the bobbed hairstyle.

The British Gazette

Published by His Majesty's Stationery Office.

LONDON, WEDNESDAY, MAY 5, 1926.

FIRST DAY OF GREAT STRIKE

Not So Complete as Hoped by its Promoters

PREMIER'S AUDIENCE OF THE KING

Miners and the General Council Meet at House of Commons

1920	Oxford University awards degrees to women
1920	First Hornby train sets produced
1921	Gordon Richards has first of 4870 wins
1921	British Legion holds its first Poppy Day
1921	Irish Free State established
1922	Tomb of King Tutankhamun discovered
1922	British Broadcasting Company established by group of wireless manufacturers
1922	'Austin Seven', the first British car for the popular market, introduced
1923	Wedding of George, Duke of York, and Lady Elizabeth Bowes-Lyon
1923	First English FA Cup final held at Wembley
1923	£50 million spent by government on unemployment relief
1923	First issue of 'Radio Times'
1923	Chimes of Big Ben first broadcast
1924	Empire Exhibition held at Wembley Stadium
1924	First Labour Government voted to power
1924	USSR recognised by British government
1926	John Logie Baird gives first public demonstration of television
1926	Princess Elizabeth born
1926	3,000,000 join in General Strike
1926	First British Motor Racing Grand Prix, held at Brooklands
1927	Transatlantic telephone service between London and New York opens
1927	First broadcast of a Football League game
1927	Automatic traffic lights come into operation
1927	First London to Brighton veteran car rally
1927	Last Model T Ford produced
1928	Alexander Fleming discovers penicillin
1929	Wall Street stock exchange 'crashes'
1929	Britain wins Schneider Trophy for seaplanes at Southampton
1929	Trial flight of airship R100

THE FAMILY IN THE 1920s

What effect did the aftermath of the First World War have on the family? Was it a decade of great changes for them?

IMPORTANT FAMILY EVENTS

NAME	DATE	EVENT

PHOTOGRAPHS

This period also has the reputation of being a time of celebration. Can anyone in the family remember (or remember being told about) the happier side of life in the twenties – cars, dancing, motion pictures?

Did anyone go to the Empire Exhibition, or the first FA Cup Final? Have you any souvenirs from the period?

THE NATION IN THE 1930s

ALONE
Music by NACIO HERB BROWN.

QUEEN MARY
STEAMING ROUND GREAT BRITAIN

INTERESTING AND

FOOTBALL POOLS
SHAKE A LINE
SAVES TIME • SAVES TROUBLE
1 2 3 4 5 6 7 8 9 10 11 12 13 14 15
THE POOL FANS FRIEND.

LITTLEWOODS FOR

FASHIONS
6d
JULY
1935

NESCAFE

Go "around the world" with SANDY POWELL
"Can you hear me, Mother?"

OLYMPIC GAMES 1936
NUMBER 1
BERLIN JUNE 1935

MY OFFER TO THE WORLD, By HITLER

SUNDAY GRAPHIC
and SUNDAY NEWS
No. 1,092. TWOPENCE.
SUNDAY, MARCH 8, 1936.

HITLER OCCUPIES RHINE
Denounced—Troops March
BIG GUNS ENTER
COLOGNE

CONFESSES
WIRELESS P.34

IN THE 1930s

- In 1931, 44,795,357 people lived in Britain.
- By 1934 there were 1,333,590 private cars.
- Typical weekly pay-packets in 1935: clerical worker £3 13s.10d.; coal miner £2 4s.8d.
- In 1932 a bottle of Gordon's Gin cost 12s.6d., 10 Players Navy Cut Cigarettes cost 6d and a Mars Bar 2d. By 1935 a pint of beer cost 7d., 1lb of tea 1s.4d., 'The Times' 4d. and inland letter postage was 1½d.
- At the cinema: *The Wizard of Oz*, *Gone with the Wind*, the Marx Brothers' *A Night at the Opera* and Walt Disney's *Snow White*.
- People were singing *On the Sunny Side of the Street*, playing Monopoly and Bezique and going to see Noel Coward's *Private Lives*.

1930	'The Times' publishes its first crossword
1930	Amy Johnson makes her solo flight to Australia
1930	R101 crash ends use of airships in Britain
1931	Highway Code introduced
1931	Gandhi visits London
1931	First 33⅓ rpm long-playing records
1932	Instant coffee first sold in Britain
1932	First Crazy Gang Show opens in London
1933	Adolf Hitler appointed German Chancellor
1933	Two British planes are first to fly over Mount Everest
1934	'Cats-eyes' laid on British roads
1934	Ocean liner SS 'Queen Mary' launched
1935	Driving tests introduced
1935	First Penguin paperbacks go on sale
1935	Silver Jubilee of King George V
1935	GPO telegram service introduced
1935	30mph speed limit introduced on roads
1936	King George V dies
1936	Coronation of King Edward VIII
1936	King Edward VIII abdicates, to marry Mrs Wallis Simpson
1936	'Speaking clock' introduced by GPO
1936	11th Olympic Games held, in Berlin
1936	Jarrow shipyard workers march 274 miles to House of Commons
1936	Fire destroys Crystal Palace
1937	Coronation of King George VI
1937	149,547 watch football match between England and Scotland
1937	999 emergency telephone service starts
1937	Billy Butlin opens his first holiday camp
1938	Nazi Germany invades Austria
1938	Women's Voluntary Service (WVS) founded
1938	Gas masks issued to school children
1939	King George VI becomes first British monarch to visit USA
1939	Imperial Airways merged with British Airways to form BOAC
1939	BBC 'Home Service' begins
1939	Hitler invades Poland, starting World War II

THE FAMILY
IN THE 1930s

This was a decade of financial difficulty for many. How did events during these years affect the family? Was anyone out of work during the Depression?

....

....

....

....

....

....

....

....

....

....

....

....

....

....

....

....

....

========== PHOTOGRAPHS ==========

≡ Important Family Events ≡

NAME	DATE	EVENT

Can anyone remember the fire at Crystal Palace? **H**ad anyone travelled by 'plane by the end of the thirties?

Did anyone hear the broadcast declaring that Britain was at war with Germany? **W**hat were the immediate effects of this announcement?

THE NATION IN THE 1940s

≡ IN THE 1940s ≡

• There was no 1941 census, but before war broke out the population was 46,466,689.

• By 1944 the number of private cars in Britain had fallen to 773,034.

• In 1948 65% of men and 41% of women smoked.

• In 1947, a train driver's weekly wage was £6 6s.6d. and a bricklayer's £5 15s.6d.

• Ration allowances per person per week in 1940 were: 8oz sugar, 2oz tea, 4oz butter and 2s.2d. worth of meat.

• The films: *Bambi, Citizen Kane, Casablanca.* The play: *An Inspector Calls.* The book: George Orwell's *Animal Farm.*

• Most toys were home-made because of the war.

1940	Sir Winston Churchill becomes Prime Minister of Coalition government
1940	Food rationing starts
1940	Home Guard formed
1940	Evacuation of British forces from Dunkirk
1940	Battle of Britain
1941	Nylon first produced in Britain, at Coventry
1941	'Bismarck' sunk by three British battleships
1941	Britain and US declare war on Japan
1942	Soap rationing begins
1943	The Mohne, Eider and Sorpe dams in Germany breached
1944	Allied Army landings in Italy begin
1944	Pay As You Earn income tax introduced
1944	Allied landings off coast of Normandy
1944	First flying bomb falls on England
1944	British airborne invasions of Arnhem and Eindhoven
1945	Yalta conference in Crimea results in founding of United Nations
1945	Hitler commits suicide
1945	War in Europe officially ends
1945	Family Allowance payment of 5s.0d. per week introduced
1945	Atomic bomb dropped on Hiroshima
1945	Japanese surrender ends World War II
1945	Bread rationing begins
1945	Bank of England nationalised
1947	Coal industry nationalised
1947	First supersonic flight
1947	Worst floods ever recorded in England
1947	School-leaving age raised to 15
1947	Princess Elizabeth marries Prince Philip
1948	Railways nationalised
1948	First full-size supermarket opens
1948	National Health Service established
1948	Bread rationing ends
1948	First Morris Minor car appears
1948	London hosts Olympic Games
1949	Clothes rationing ends
1949	First comprehensive school opens
1949	North Atlantic Treaty Organisation (NATO) created

THE FAMILY
IN THE 1940s

How did the Second World War change the family's life? Who fought in the War? Were there any casualties?

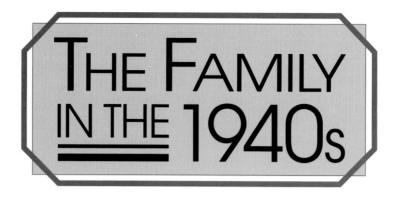

PHOTOGRAPHS

═ IMPORTANT FAMILY EVENTS ═

NAME	DATE	EVENT

What was it like for those left behind? Were any of the young ones evacuated? Where did they go? How did those left at home cope with war-time life?

What was it like when the war ended? What was the spirit of the country at that time? How soon did life begin to return to normal?

THE NATION IN THE 1950s

LIVE IT UPS

FESTIVAL OF BRITAIN 1951

BILL HALEY AND HIS COMETS

EXTENDED PLAY RECORD

Nº 18

Made by Kodak 'BROWNIE' 127 camera

24/6 INC. TAX

EXCITING GLAMOUR PHOTOS

Marilyn MONROE

The new Sensational Dansette

Picture Show
THE PAPER FOR PEOPLE WHO GO TO THE PICTURES

FINAL NIGHT EXTRA

Evening Standard
FRIDAY, FEBRUARY 8, 1952 • Three-halfpence

On the roofs, on the balconies, in the people crowd to hear the Pro

GOD SAVE THE QUEEN

Elizabeth R CORONATION TUESDAY 2 JUNE 1953

IN THE 1950s

- The 1951 census totalled 48,854,303.
- By 1954 there were 3,172,869 cars in Britain.
- In 1953, 59% of men and 36% of women smoked.
- Wages rose rapidly: in 1955 a clerical worker could expect to earn £10 1s.0d. a week, a coal miner £8 6s.0d., and a solicitor £2086 a year.
- Prices rose too: by 1955 a pint of beer had gone up to 1s.3$\frac{1}{4}$d., 1lb of tea to 4s.6d. and inland letter post to 2$\frac{1}{2}$d. A Kodak Brownie Box camera cost £1 19s.9d., a 'Noddy' soft toy £1, and a Dansette Radiogram £31 10s.0d.
- Top children's names in 1950: Susan and David.
- Films of the 50s: *The Ten Commandments*, *High Society* and *East of Eden*.

1950	Election returns televised in Britain for first time
1950	Petrol and soap rationing ends
1950	India becomes a democratic Republic
1950	Coronation Stone stolen from Westminster Abbey
1950	Marcus Morris, a clergyman, founds 'Eagle' comic
1951	First Miss World contest
1951	Festival of Britain, to mark centenary of the Great Exhibition
1951	First zebra crossings
1952	Death of King George VI
1952	Identity cards abolished in Britain
1952	Last London tram runs
1952	BBC radio broadcasts first 'Goon Show'
1953	Sugar and sweet rationing ends
1953	Edmund Hillary and Sherpa Tensing climb Everest
1953	Coronation of HM Queen Elizabeth II
1954	Roger Bannister runs a mile in under four minutes
1954	Bill Haley's 'Rock Around the Clock' recorded – the best-selling pop record of all time
1954	All food rationing ends
1955	First commercial appears on television
1956	First yellow 'no parking' lines
1956	Premium Bonds go on sale
1956	First Eurovision song contest
1957	The Queen makes her first Christmas television broadcast
1958	Prince Charles created Prince of Wales
1958	Eight Manchester United players die in aircraft crash
1958	9000 join first CND protest march from London to Aldermaston
1958	Parking meters come into operation
1958	Debutantes presented at Court for the last time
1958	First women peers in the House of Lords
1958	Work starts on Forth Road Bridge
1959	First section of the M1 motorway opened
1959	Postcodes added to all addresses

THE FAMILY
IN THE 1950s

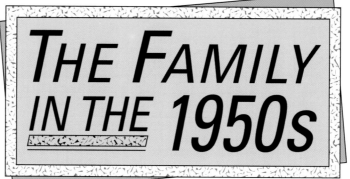

*M*any remember this as a decade of optimism and rising standards of living. *W*hat events do the family recall?

....
....
....
....
....
....
....
....
....
....
....

IMPORTANT FAMILY EVENTS

NAME	DATE	EVENT

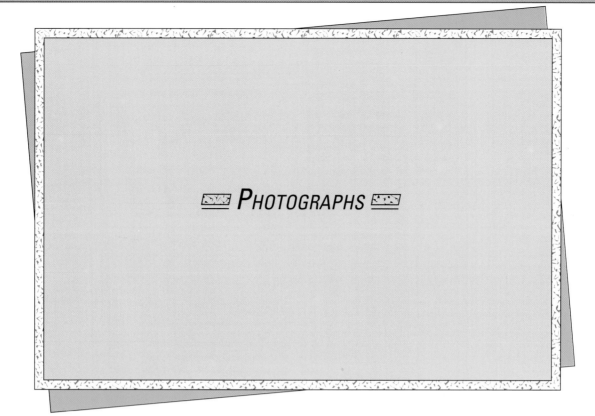

✧ *PHOTOGRAPHS* ✧

*W*hat are the family's memories of the death of King George VI and of H.M. Queen Elizabeth II's coronation?

....

....

....

....

....

....

*T*his was the decade in which commercial television started, the first motorway was built, the last London tram ran and package holidays started. *H*ow did all this affect the family?

....

....

....

....

....

The Nation in the 1960s

PARLOPHONE

THE BEATLES

No. 1

HER STANDING THERE
MISERY • ANNA • CHAINS

mono

mono

Twist and Shout ★ The Beatles

Twist and Shout
THE BEATLES

RADIO CAROLINE

THE ALL DAY
MUSIC STATION

Featuring
the TOP
DEE JAYS
and new
personal
stories of
the STARS

WORLD CUP WILLIE

Published with

by Syd Green

DINKY TOYS

CORGI TOYS

NEWS OF THE WORLD

EMPIRE NEWS No. 6,239. PRICE SIXPENCE

SUNDAY, JUNE 9, 1963

Confessions of Christine

BY

CORONATION STREET

SPEAR

PRODUCTION

JULES RIMET CUP
WORLD CHAMPIONSHIP
ENGLAND 1966 JULY 11-30

EVERTON · SHEFFIELD · SUNDERLAND · ASTON VILLA · MANCHESTER · MIDDLESBROUGH · WHITE CITY

Queen
Elizabeth 2

CUNARD

WATNEY MANN
WORLD CUP ALE
SPECIAL
PALE ALE

❀❀ IN THE 1960s ❀❀

- In 1961 the UK population was 51,283,892.
- By 1964 there were 8,436,193 private cars, a police constable's weekly wage was £13 9s.6d. and a bricklayer's £17 3s.0d. 54% of men and 41% of women smoked.
- By '65 a pint of beer cost 1s.9d., 1lb of tea 8s.0d., 'The Times' 6d. and an inland letter 3d. A gallon of petrol cost 5s.2d. and a Mini Cooper £679.
- The most popular name for a girl born in 1965 was Tracey.
- Hits of the 60s: TV: *Coronation Street* and *Thunderbirds*. Pop Music: The Beatles. Toys: Sindy and Action Man. Fashion: Mary Quant. Films: *The Sound of Music*, *The Seven Year Itch* and *Mary Poppins*. Plays: *West Side Story* and *The Caretaker*.

SOUVENIR PROGRAMME

PRICE 2/6

DAVID TOFF MUSIC PUBLISHING CO. LTD. LO

BACKING BRITAIN

THUNDERBIRDS
STICKER FUN BOOK

I'M ALL RIGHT JACK
TEMPORARY FAULT
S.O.S.

The time: 9.18 pm, July 20, AD 1969

MAN ON THE MOON

THE MOON

MAN on the MOON
CHEWING GUM
7 CA...

TWIGGY

the seven year itch

1960	MOT tests on motor vehicles introduced
1960	Hovercraft enters commercial service
1960	First traffic wardens appear in London
1960	Britain's first nuclear-powered submarine launched
1961	*New English Bible* published
1961	Cash betting at betting shops made legal
1962	Trolleybuses run for the last time in London
1962	First James Bond film, 'Dr No', released
1963	£2,631,684 stolen from Post Office train in the Great Train Robbery
1963	President Kennedy assassinated in Dallas
1963	Christine Keeler jailed in Profumo Affair trial
1963	'From Me to You' becomes the first of four successive number one hits for The Beatles
1964	Harold Wilson becomes Prime Minister
1964	Sir Winston Churchill makes his last appearance in the House of Commons
1964	Radio Caroline starts transmission
1965	Sir Winston Churchill dies, aged 90
1965	Cigarette advertisements banned on TV
1965	70mph speed limit introduced
1966	Seaman's strike, the longest in Britain since World War II
1966	England hosts and wins the football World Cup
1966	Severn Bridge opens
1967	First North Sea gas pumped ashore
1967	Oil tanker 'Torrey Canyon' wrecked on the Pollard Rock
1967	Francis Chichester sails round the world solo
1967	British liner 'QE2' launched
1967	BBC Radio 1 goes on air
1968	Abortion legalised
1969	Investiture of Prince of Wales at Caernarfon Castle
1969	Neil Armstrong sets foot on the moon
1969	First colour television programmes broadcast
1969	Abolition of the death penalty for murder

JULIE ANDREWS
A SHOWTIME SOUVENIR

The Family in the 1960s

Who remembers England winning the Football World Cup? **O**r seeing pictures of Neil Armstrong walking on the moon?

◦◦ Photographs ◦◦

✿✿ Important Family Events ✿✿

NAME	DATE	EVENT

Does anyone remember where they were and what they were doing when they heard that President Kennedy had been killed?

What are other memories of this decade, the Swinging Sixties?

The Nation in the 1970s

Cadbury's Fruit & Nut
1/-
5P
BOURNVILLE CHOCOLATE

3p

Your guide to decimal currency in the Post Office.

DECIMAL COINAGE CONVERTER

All change!

Mail
9p

MOUNTBATTEN SPECIAL ISSUE

DECIMAL DAY
MONDAY 15th FEBRUARY 1971

MURDER OF LORD LOUIS
Mountbatten

The Silver Jubilee Project Book

1952 THE QUEENS SILVER JUBILEE 1977

U.S.S. ENTERPRISE
NCC-1701

STAR TREK
NCC-1701
ANN

ENTERPRISE & SPACE LAB
The World's First Reusable Orbital System!
esa

✪ In the 1970s ✪

- By 1971 the population was 53,978,538.
- In 1974 there were 13,947,934 cars in Britain.
- From '70 to '75 a coal miner's weekly wage increased from £16 0s.0d. to £127.70, and a farm worker's from £13 3s.0d. to £66.90.
- Prices also rose: between '71 and '79 the cost of a pint of beer rose from 12p to 34p, 1lb tea from 28p to 35p, 'The Times' from 5p to 15p and inland postage from 3p to 10p. A Mars Bar rose from 4p to 13p.
- Film successes: *Star Wars*, *The Sting* and *The Godfather*. TV favourites: *Starsky & Hutch* and *Star Trek*. Pop Groups: The Osmonds and The Bay City Rollers. Crazes: Skateboards, hot pants, personal calculators, Smurfs and Playpeople.

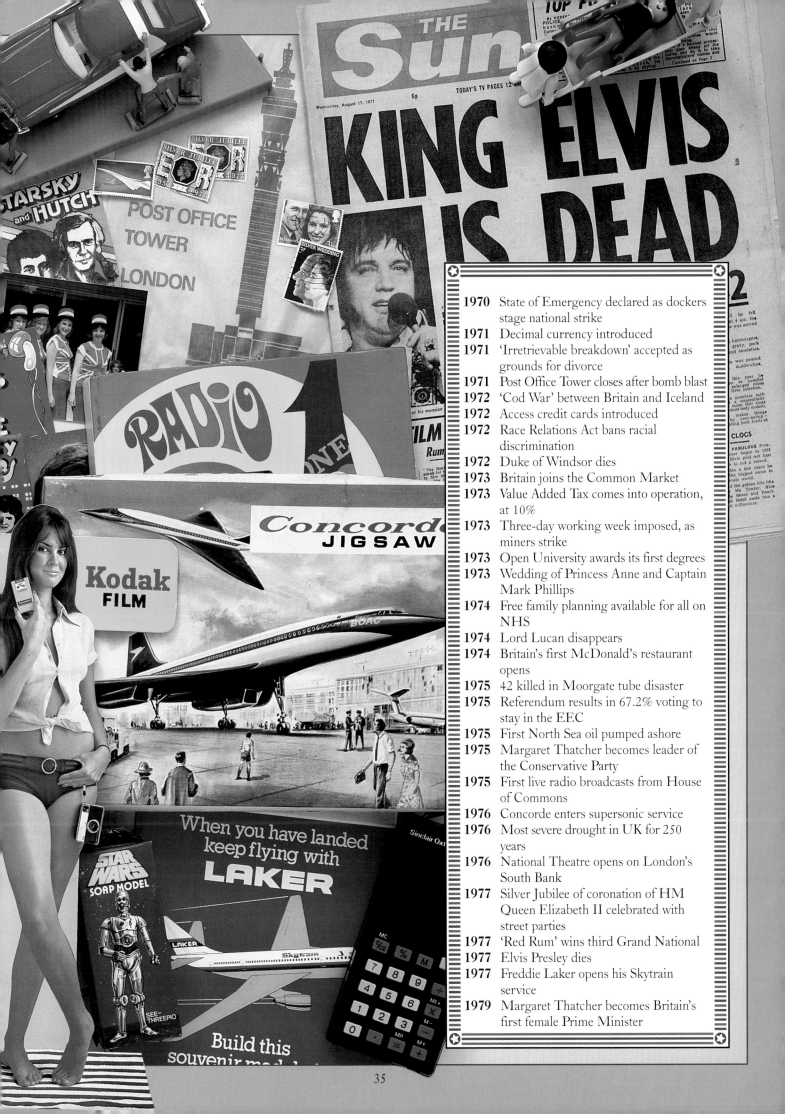

Year	Event
1970	State of Emergency declared as dockers stage national strike
1971	Decimal currency introduced
1971	'Irretrievable breakdown' accepted as grounds for divorce
1971	Post Office Tower closes after bomb blast
1972	'Cod War' between Britain and Iceland
1972	Access credit cards introduced
1972	Race Relations Act bans racial discrimination
1972	Duke of Windsor dies
1973	Britain joins the Common Market
1973	Value Added Tax comes into operation, at 10%
1973	Three-day working week imposed, as miners strike
1973	Open University awards its first degrees
1973	Wedding of Princess Anne and Captain Mark Phillips
1974	Free family planning available for all on NHS
1974	Lord Lucan disappears
1974	Britain's first McDonald's restaurant opens
1975	42 killed in Moorgate tube disaster
1975	Referendum results in 67.2% voting to stay in the EEC
1975	First North Sea oil pumped ashore
1975	Margaret Thatcher becomes leader of the Conservative Party
1975	First live radio broadcasts from House of Commons
1976	Concorde enters supersonic service
1976	Most severe drought in UK for 250 years
1976	National Theatre opens on London's South Bank
1977	Silver Jubilee of coronation of HM Queen Elizabeth II celebrated with street parties
1977	'Red Rum' wins third Grand National
1977	Elvis Presley dies
1977	Freddie Laker opens his Skytrain service
1979	Margaret Thatcher becomes Britain's first female Prime Minister

The Family in the 1970s

A period of social unrest and change – the miners' strike, the three-day week, the Vietnam War. **W**hat was it like for the family?

....

....

....

....

....

....

....

....

....

....

✪ Important Family Events ✪

NAME	DATE	EVENT

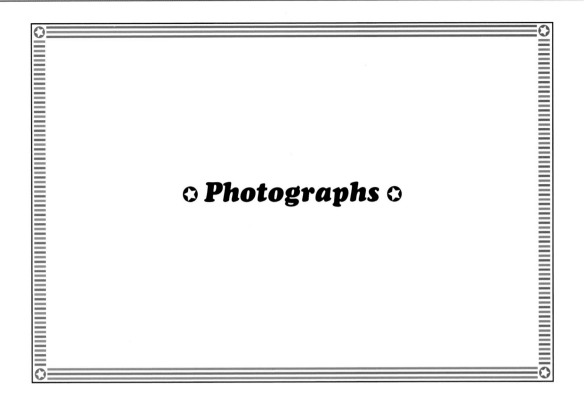

What memories are there of decimalisation and of Britain joining the EEC?

....

....

....

....

....

....

What were the happiest things that happened to the family in the 70s? **D**oes anyone remember street parties for the Queen's Silver Jubilee?

....

....

....

....

....

The Nation in the 1980s

TODAY
TUESDAY MARCH 4, 1986, 18 PENCE

THE TIMES

The Toxteth riot: call for troops on standby

Missiles fly as looters resume battle with Liverpool police

From Nicholas Timmins, Craig Seton and Arthur Osman, Liverpool

FAIR PLAY BINGO
★★★★★
CAN WIN
NDS WITH

Watch your favourite newspapers for the starting date

The Mirror
PLUS THE
★ WIN A
£ MILLIO
★ GAME

SUNDAY Mirror Pa

HIS CARD IS VALUABL

THE FALKLANDS WAR
A Visual Diary

SONY
STEREO
WALKMAN

JULY 1981
50p

Mrs Thatcher and Mr Gorbachev yesterday

Maggie's nuclear sparring match

CHRIS BUCK
Political Editor

SOLD FOR £24,750,000
(Yours here for only 20p)

Topps
SPITTING IMAGE
PICTURE CARDS & BUBBLE GUM

In the 1980s

• In 1981 the population was 54,147,300.
• There were 18,531,744 private cars in 1984 and 34% of the population smoked.
• Between '80 and '89 prices rose: the average house from £27,244 to £74,976; a Mars Bar from 14p to 20p; a pint of beer from 40p to 87p; 1lb tea from 88p to £1.24 and a stamp from 12p to 20p.
• The most popular names for babies born in 1981 were Sarah and Andrew.
• Film of the 80s: *E.T.* Pop stars of the 80s: Michael Jackson, Madonna, Dire Straits, UB40 and The Police. Fads of the 80s: Psion Organisers, Punk, Spitting Image, Trivial Pursuit and Filofaxes.

1980	SAS storms Iranian Embassy and releases hostages
1980	John Lennon shot dead
1980	Bjorn Borg wins Wimbledon for 5th time
1981	First London Marathon
1981	Prince Charles marries Lady Diana Spencer
1981	SDP launched by Labour defectors
1981	First reports of AIDS
1981	Worst riots of century, at Toxteth, Liverpool
1982	Falklands War against Argentina
1982	Pope John Paul II visits Britain
1982	Channel 4 begins broadcasting
1983	Wearing seat-belts in cars made compulsory
1983	One pound coins introduced
1983	Jane Torville and Christopher Dean win third consecutive World Ice Dance title
1983	Conservatives win General Election
1984	Miners' strike
1984	Inaugural flight of Virgin Atlantic
1984	Robert Maxwell buys 'The Mirror'
1985	'Live Aid' pop concert raises more than £50 million for famine relief in Africa
1985	GLC abolished
1985	Start of BBC's 'EastEnders'
1986	Channel Tunnel agreement signed
1986	Corporal punishment abolished in schools
1986	'Today', Britain's first colour newspaper, published
1986	Wedding of Prince Andrew and Sarah Ferguson
1987	Terry Waite disappears in Beirut
1987	'Herald of Free Enterprise' capsizes in Zeebrugge, with loss of 193 lives
1987	'Sunflowers' by Vincent van Gogh sold for £24,750,000
1987	Hurricane force winds kill 19
1987	Margaret Thatcher wins her third General Election
1988	GCSEs replace 'O' levels
1989	Overcrowding at Hillsborough Football Stadium kills 95

The Family in the 1980s

Much came to be taken for granted in the 80s: colour televisions, washing machines, foreign holidays, a generally rising standard of living for most people. What were your impressions of it all?

Photographs

Important Family Events

NAME	DATE	EVENT

Dramatic international events included the Falklands War, the Iranian Embassy siege and hostages being taken in Beirut. What was going on in the family's life?

Does anyone remember the early years of the London Marathon, or celebrating the wedding of Prince Charles and Lady Diana, or seeing Pope John Paul when he visited Britain?

the nation in the 1990s

◄ ◄ in the 1990s ► ►

- In 1991 the population was 54,156,067.
- By 1994 there were 23,831,906 cars and only 27% of the population smoked.
- Basic prices in 1993: a pint of beer cost £1.19, 250gm tea 74p, 'The Times' 30p, and a 1st class stamp 25p, the same as a Mars Bar.
- Pop groups: Oasis, Blur and The Spice Girls.
- Films: *Jurrassic Park*, *Reservoir Dogs*, *Toy Story* and *101 Dalmatians*. On stage: *Riverdance* (and *Phantom/Cats/Miss Saigon* etc.). Flops: *Eldorado*. Innovations: alcoholic 'soft' drinks, Wallace & Gromitt, mobile phones, laptop computers, personal CD players, disposable cameras. Toys: Teenage Mutant Hero Turtles, Pogs, Sony PlayStations.

1990	John Major succeeds Margaret Thatcher as Prime Minister
1990	300,000 in riots against Poll Tax
1990	46 die in gales across England
1991	John McCarthy and Terry Waite released
1992	Operation 'Desert Storm' frees Kuwait in Gulf War
1992	Nigel Mansell wins Formula One world championship
1992	Fire destroys part of Windsor Castle
1992	Betty Boothroyd becomes first woman Speaker of House of Commons
1992	UK leaves European Monetary System
1993	Buckingham Palace opens to tourists
1993	Anti-terrorist cordon drawn around the City of London
1994	Inauguration of Channel Tunnel
1994	Church of England ordains women as priests
1994	Shops allowed to open on Sundays
1994	IRA announces total ceasefire
1994	£7 million spent on first day of National Lottery ticket sales
1995	Barings bank collapses, losing £650m
1995	England wins Five-Nations Rugby Cup
1995	First 'Eurostar' trains run through Channel Tunnel
1996	BSE scare causes ban on British beef in Europe (and McDonalds)
1996	Duke and Duchess of York divorce
1996	Prince Charles and Princess Diana divorce
1996	16 children killed by gunman at Dunblane school
1996	Nelson Mandela visits UK as South African President
1996	Britain hosts 'Euro 96' football championships
1997	66% vote for monarchy in largest TV poll
1997	Tony Blair becomes Prime Minister in Labour landslide
1997	Princess Diana killed in Paris car accident
1998	IRA signs 'Good Friday' ceasefire agreement
1999	Nato bombs Serbia
1999	Prince Edward marries Sophie Rhys-Jones

the family in the 1990s

W̲hat are your happiest memories of family life in the 1990s?

....

....

....

....

....

....

....

....

....

....

◄◄ important family events ►►

NAME	DATE	EVENT

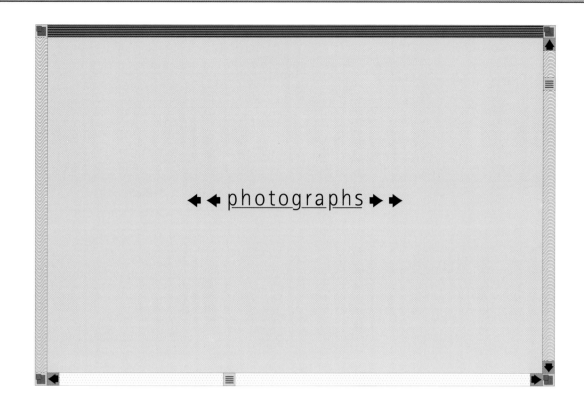

**W**ere any people known to the family involved in the Gulf War, or other major events of the decade?

**W**hat do you think the 'nineties will be most remembered for in thirty years time?

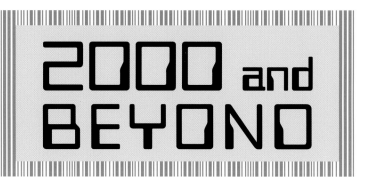

2000 and BEYOND

Which family events are you looking forward to during the next few years?

How did you celebrate the start of the new millenium?

What are your hopes for the family, the nation and the world in the twenty-first century?

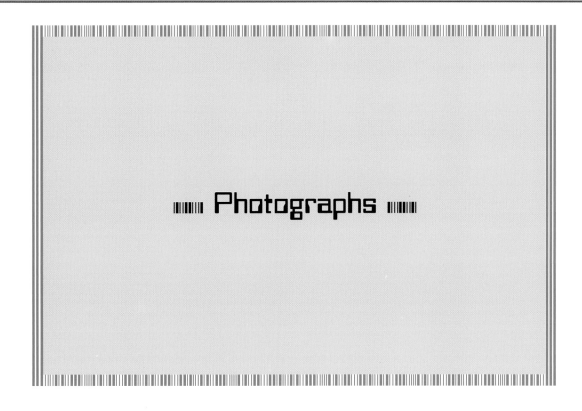

Photographs

Note below, as they occur, the family, national and international events you think future members of the family will regard as having been significant.

FAMILY EVENTS	NATIONAL EVENTS	INTERNATIONAL EVENTS

YOUR GREAT-GRANDFATHER'S BROTHERS AND SISTERS
Your Great-Great-Uncles and Great-Great-Aunts

YOUR FATHER'S FATHER'S FATHER
Your Great-Grandfather

YOUR GREAT-GRANDMOTHER'S BROTHERS AND SISTERS
Your Great-Great-Uncles and Great-Great-Aunts

YOUR FATHER'S FATHER'S MOTHER
Your Great-Grandmother

YOUR GREAT-GRANDFATHER'S BROTHERS AND SISTERS
Your Great-Great-Uncles and Great-Great-Aunts

YOUR FATHER'S MOTHER'S FATHER
Your Great-Grandfather

YOUR GREAT-GRANDMOTHER'S BROTHERS AND SISTERS
Your Great-Great-Uncles and Great-Great-Aunts

YOUR FATHER'S MOTHER'S MOTHER
Your Great-Grandmother

YOUR GREAT-GRANDFATHER'S BROTHERS AND SISTERS
Your Great-Great-Uncles and Great-Great-Aunts

YOUR MOTHER'S FATHER'S FATHER
Your Great-Grandfather

YOUR GREAT-GRANDMOTHER'S BROTHERS AND SISTERS
Your Great-Great-Uncles and Great-Great-Aunts

YOUR MOTHER'S FATHER'S MOTHER
Your Great-Grandmother

YOUR GREAT-GRANDFATHER'S BROTHERS AND SISTERS
Your Great-Great-Uncles and Great-Great-Aunts

YOUR MOTHER'S MOTHER'S FATHER
Your Great-Grandfather

YOUR GREAT-GRANDMOTHER'S BROTHERS AND SISTERS
Your Great-Great-Uncles and Great-Great-Aunts

YOUR MOTHER'S MOTHER'S MOTHER
Your Great-Grandmother

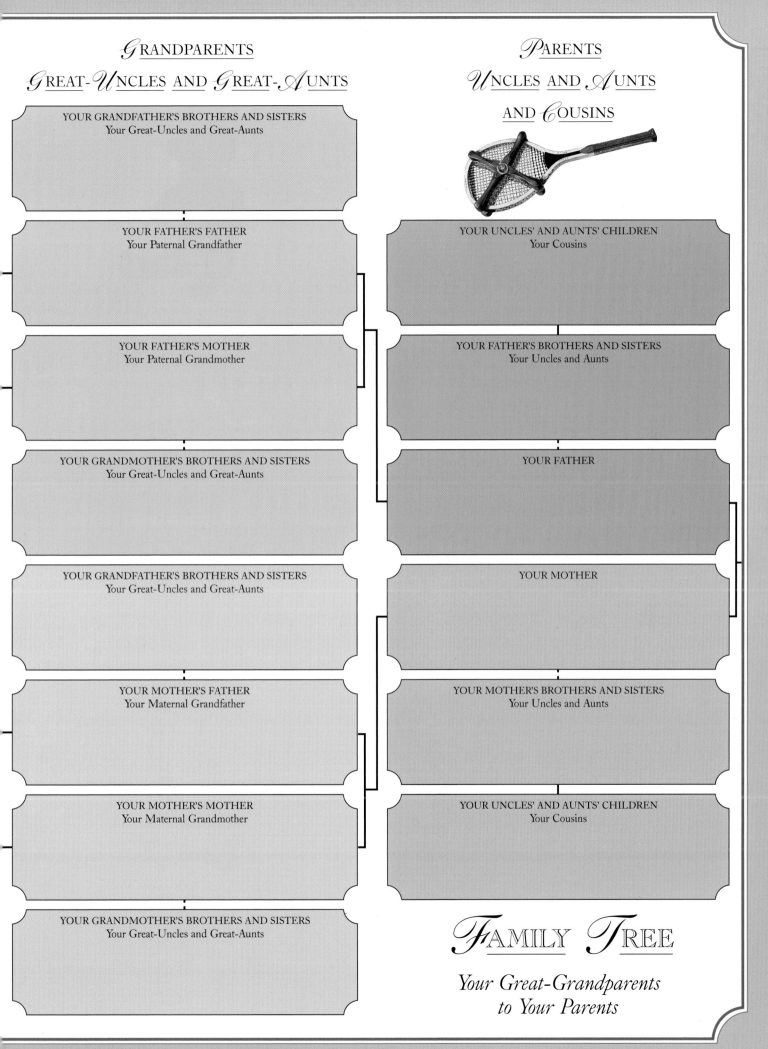

YOUR GRANDFATHER'S BROTHERS AND SISTERS
Your Great-Uncles and Great-Aunts

YOUR FATHER'S FATHER
Your Paternal Grandfather

YOUR UNCLES' AND AUNTS' CHILDREN
Your Cousins

YOUR FATHER'S MOTHER
Your Paternal Grandmother

YOUR FATHER'S BROTHERS AND SISTERS
Your Uncles and Aunts

YOUR GRANDMOTHER'S BROTHERS AND SISTERS
Your Great-Uncles and Great-Aunts

YOUR FATHER

YOUR GRANDFATHER'S BROTHERS AND SISTERS
Your Great-Uncles and Great-Aunts

YOUR MOTHER

YOUR MOTHER'S FATHER
Your Maternal Grandfather

YOUR MOTHER'S BROTHERS AND SISTERS
Your Uncles and Aunts

YOUR MOTHER'S MOTHER
Your Maternal Grandmother

YOUR UNCLES' AND AUNTS' CHILDREN
Your Cousins

YOUR GRANDMOTHER'S BROTHERS AND SISTERS
Your Great-Uncles and Great-Aunts

FAMILY TREE

*Your Great-Grandparents
to Your Parents*

YOUR NEPHEWS AND NIECES
Your Brothers' and Sisters' Children

YOUR BROTHERS AND SISTERS

YOURSELF

YOUR CHILDREN

YOUR SPOUSE

YOUR SPOUSE'S BROTHERS AND SISTERS

YOUR SPOUSE'S NEPHEWS AND NIECES
Your Spouse's Brothers' and Sisters' Children

Family *Tree*

Yourself and Your Spouse
to Your Great-Grandchildren

GRANDCHILDREN

YOUR CHILDREN'S CHILDREN

GREAT-GRANDCHILDREN

YOUR GRANDCHILDREN'S CHILDREN

OTHER RELATIONS

'Other relations' might include your own or your childrens' godparents and guardians, your second cousins, children to whom you are yourself a godparent or a guardian, and any step-relations. This page is for your memories of them.

PHOTOGRAPH

SPECIAL FRIENDS

For notes and memories about the other people who have played an important part in the family's life, but are not related to you by birth or marriage. Old friends from schooldays who became unofficial 'aunts' and 'uncles' to children and grandchildren, people you have come to know well at work or socially . . . in fact anyone who has been important in your life, or particularly valued as a friend, may find a place here.

PHOTOGRAPH

ADDITIONAL PHOTOGRAPHS

ADDITIONAL PHOTOGRAPHS

ADDITIONAL PHOTOGRAPHS